To . . . .

From . . . .

HORSES
a guide to carrots, cantering, and sugar cubes

by Mark Dunne

LAUREL
GLEN

Horse and humans have lived together for thousands of years—and yet what goes on between a horse's ears, its hopes and fears, dreams and desires, are still largely a mystery. Hopefully this little book will go some way to uncovering the rich and complex world of an intensely thoughtful and noble creature...

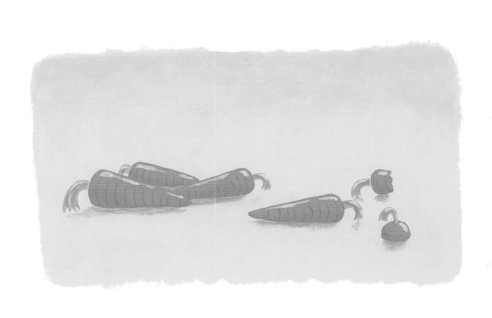

Contents

The Versatile Horse

Throughout history horses have been...

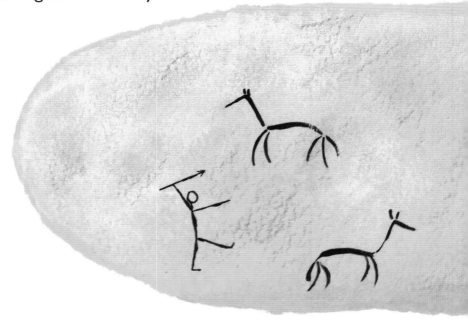

...painted on walls

...made of wood

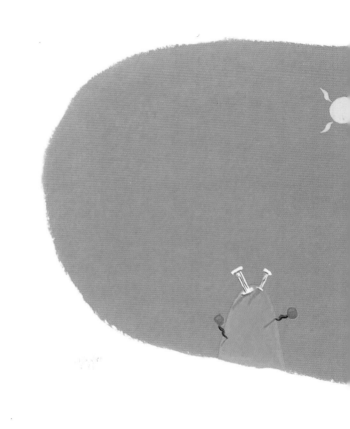

...mythical creatures

...friends to the famous

...daring messagers

...beasts of burden

...law enforcers

...entertainers

...sport stars

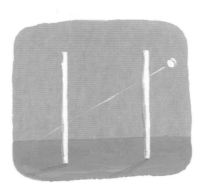

Comforts of Home

Horses love…

...their neighbors

...grooming

...winning

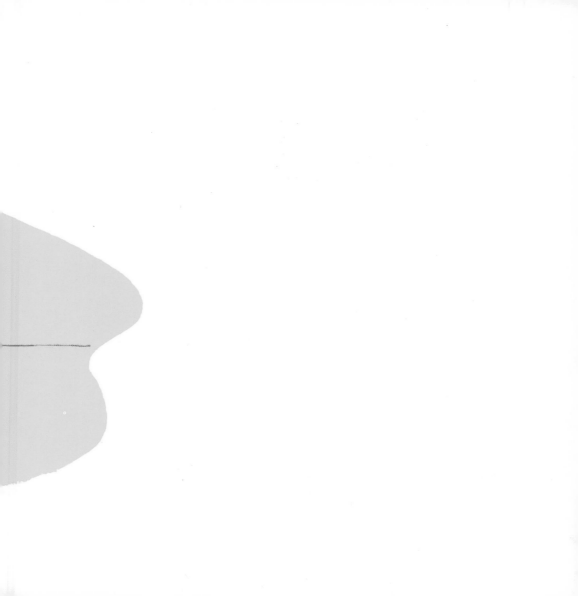

...haute cuisine

hay

grass

sugar cubes

feed bags

and of course carrots!

Horses love exercise:

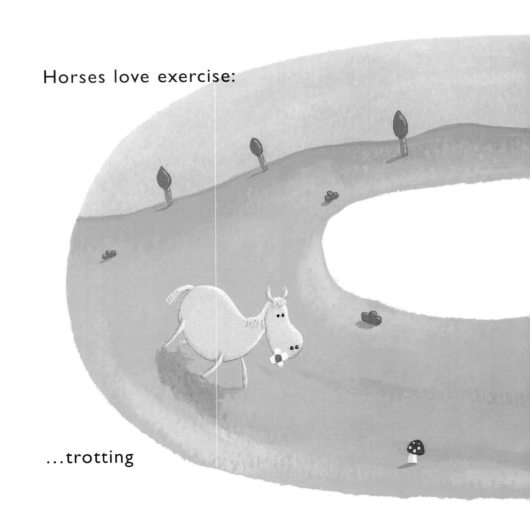

...trotting

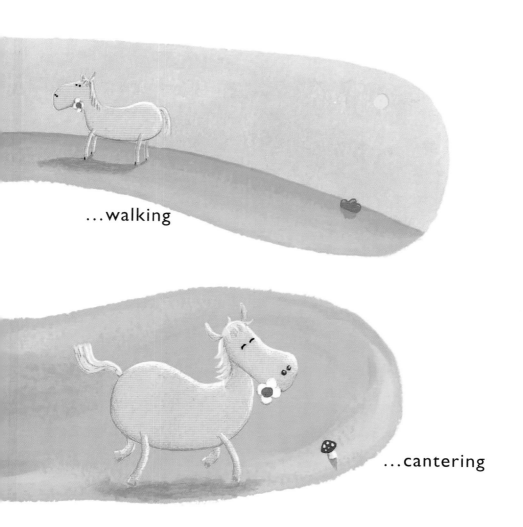

...walking

...cantering

...galloping

...and none of the above

(horses can be stubborn)

Horsing Around

Flicking away flies...

...true friends are made.

Horses like a variety of footwear.

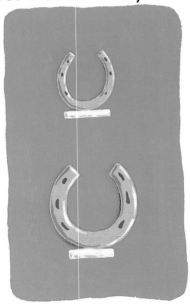

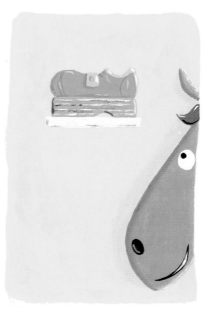

?

...blankets in cold weather

...and hats in hot weather!

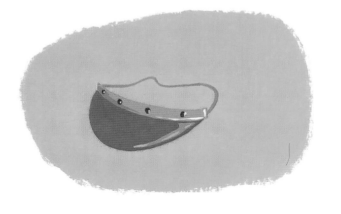

Games horses play:

hide and seek

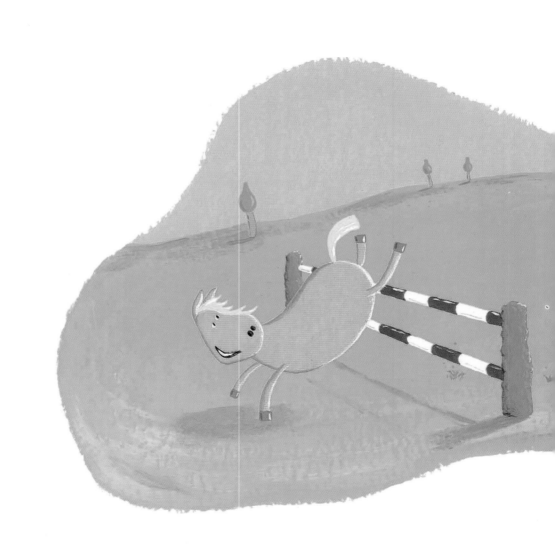

jumping...

...and not jumping

frolicking

...and meditating

Anatomy

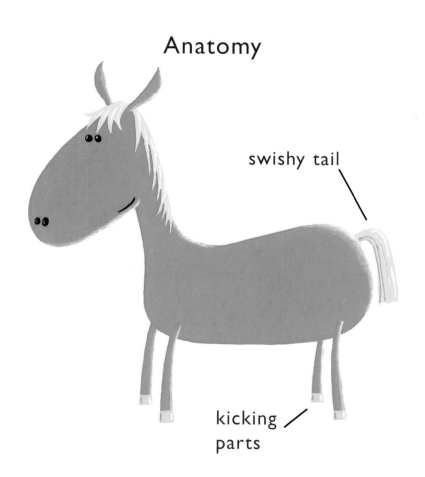

swishy tail

kicking
parts

Horses come in a variety of heights,

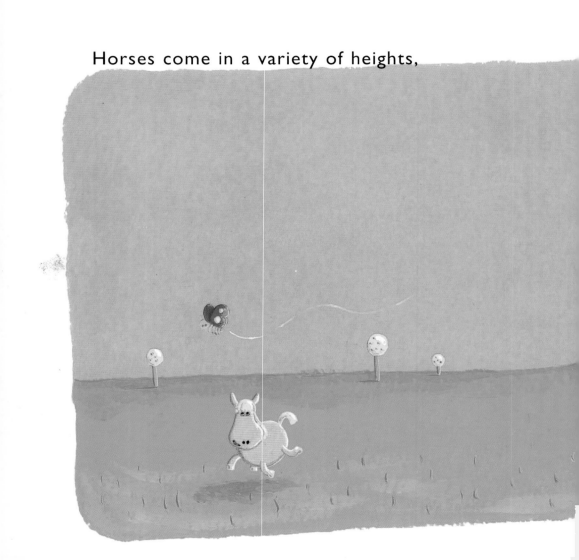

...widths,

...looks,

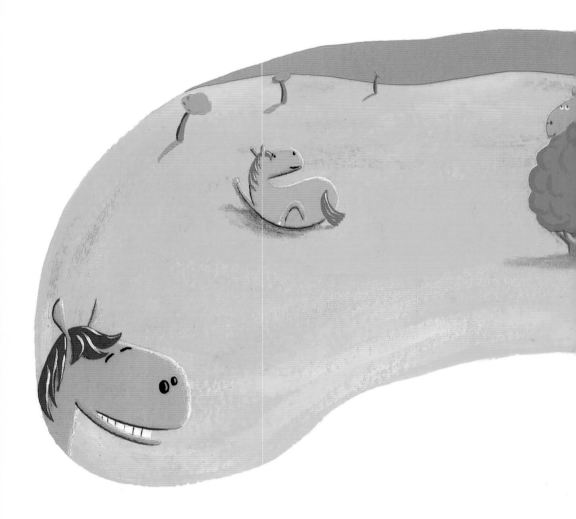

...and colors.

with different markings...

star

stripe

blaze

snip

Horses communicate
through sound...

blow

neigh

whinny

snort

...and ear movement

pricked

floppy

radar

airplane

with their tails...

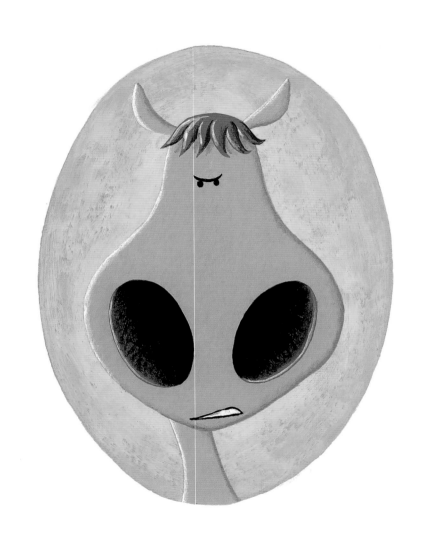

even their nostrils!

Horse Dreams

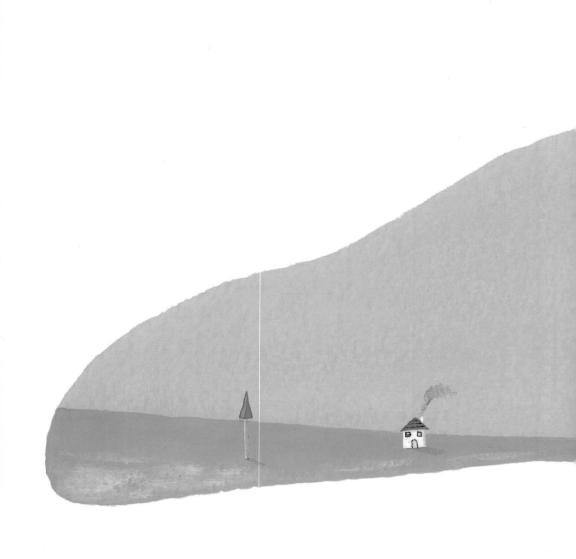

To fly like Pegasus

To sleep in a real bed

To jump the highest...

...and run the fastest

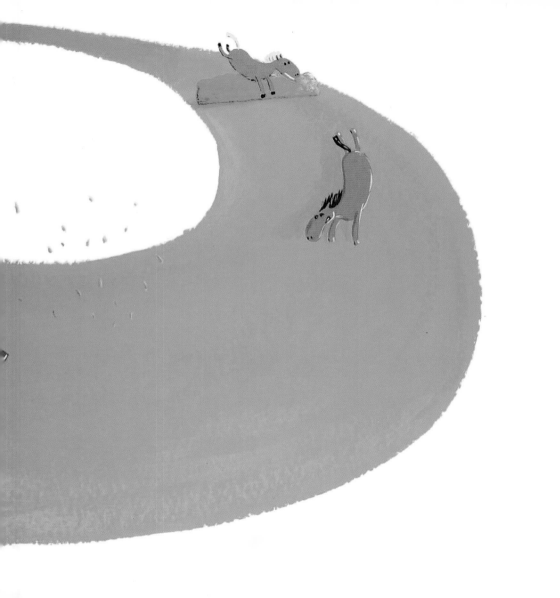

To visit sugar cube mountain

To dance like the horses in Vienna

To have a position of power

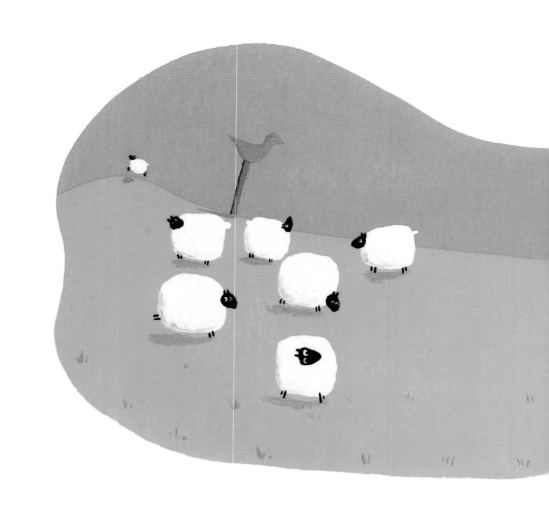

To be a sheep-horse

To run free with the herd

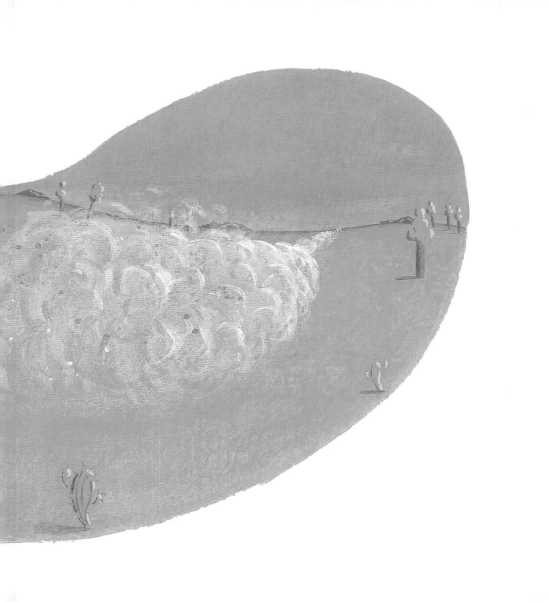

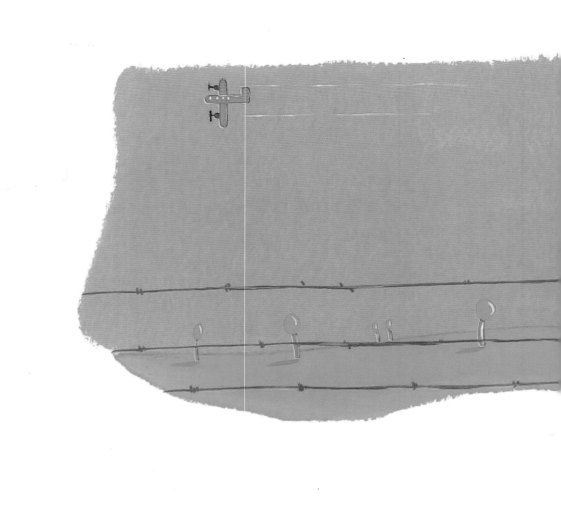

But who needs more than a field on a sunny day?

About The Artist

Artist Mark Dunne studied in Bootle and Wolverhampton where he learned the simple pleasures of shapes and colors. He lives in London with his friends Mac the dog, Josh the frog, and Faye the squirrel. His favorite number is 18,769.

First published in the United States in 2000 by
Laurel Glen Publishing
An imprint of the Advantage Publishers Group
5880 Oberlin Drive
San Diego, CA 92121-4794
www.advantagebooksonline.com

Publisher Allen Orso
Managing Editor JoAnn Padgett
Project Editor Elizabeth McNulty

Author/illustrator inquiries, and questions about permissions and rights should be addressed to MQ Publications Ltd, 254–258 Goswell Road, London EC1V 7RL; e-mail: mqp@btinternet.com

ISBN: 1-57145-659-7
Library of Congress Cataloging in Publication Data available upon request.

Printed in Italy

1 2 3 4 5   00 01 02 03 04